CW00395084

Paws for Shakespeare

MAUREEN MELVIN

Illustrated by Geoff Crook

CASILDA BOOKS

Published by
Casilda Books
PO Box 241
Petersfield
GU32 9EA

www.maureenmelvin.com

ISBN 978-0-957 0117-1-7

Published 2011

Typeset, printed and bound in Great Britain by
KerryType Ltd., Midhurst, W. Sussex, GU29 9PX

Also by Maureen Melvin

with illustrations by Geoff Crook

PAWS FOR THOUGHT
PAWS AGAIN
PAWS FOR PASTA
PAWS FOREVER

For Sophia

We thought you'd be a puppy dog
Like Alice or like me.
We must have got our thinking caps askew!
But now that you're a tiny girl
We're pleased as we can be
So here is *Paws for Shakespeare* just for you.

Contents

Puddles
by Alice

I don't like drinking out of bowls
But puddles is delishus,
Though Annie says they're full of germs
And not at all newtrishus.

Well, I've seen newts in puddles, yes,
And water-boatmen too
And sticklebacks and dragon-flies,
They seem to struggle through.

But I'm a green, organic dog
Which puts me on the map.
While Annabel is quite content
With water from the tap.

So when she puts the kettle on
And calls me in for tea,
I turn my head the other way
'Cos puddles is for me.

Wits' End

by Annabel

Mummy's at her Wits' End
She must be in a tizz;
She goes there when she's angry
But we don't know where it is.

She says we drive her to it
But we don't go in the car.
I don't think it's a nice place
But it isn't very far.

Sometimes it's in her bedroom
And sometimes in the bath.
Sometimes it's in the potting shed
Or up the garden path.

We've never seen a signpost
Except in Mummy's eyes,
So one day, when we find it,
We'll have a big surprise!

But when she's back from Wits' End,
It's joy and jamboree
And hugs and kisses for us both
And Something Nice for tea.

Pickle

by Alice

Mummy calls me Pickle!
It's not my proper name.
She does it when we're naughty
And it's me wot gets the blame.

I've found a jar of pickles
It's on the kitchen shelf.
The label nearly foxed me
But I cracked it by myself.

I've seen them using pickles
In sandwiches and such.
And something called a Ploughman's Lunch,
A dish I would not touch.

On one thing I'm determined:
However bad I am,
I won't be served up on a cart
With cheddar cheese and ham.

"NO, ALICE, I TOLD YOU -
IT'S 'À LA CARTE'!"

Forty Winks

by Annabel

What does it mean – this 'Forty Winks'
Can anyone explain?
She settles in an easy chair,
We watch and wait, in vain.

And when it's time to hit the trail,
It's something of a jinx.
'I'll take you later on,' she'll say,
'I'll just have Forty Winks.'

It isn't like a night-time sleep
When everything is dark.
It only lasts a little while,
She wakens if we bark.

We sit together, side by side
And watch her like a lynx.
Her eyelids never move at all,
No sign of Forty Winks.

We went to see the tawny owl
To ask him what he thinks
And if he'd ever come across
This thing called 'Forty Winks'.

He fixed us with a solemn stare
And sat there like a sphinx –
Will no-one ever tell us what
They mean by 'Forty Winks'?

Bad Habits

by Alice

Annie, for all her snooty ways,
Has very nasty habits.
It's one thing tucking into treats
So kindly left by rabbits.

But Annie likes to roam the fields
Where cows and horses graze
And there she feasts on you know what
Which blows her out for days.

She doesn't only eat the stuff,
She rolls in it as well!
She really lets the side down
And I can't abide the smell.

And when we march her down the lane
To find the garden hose,
I walk on Mummy's other side
And try to hold my nose.

Daddy is…

by Annabel

Daddy is: snuggles and cuddles in bed
And 'Keep clear of the newspapers, Girls'.
And splashing of suds when he lands in the tub
As the bath water swishes and swirls.

Daddy is: comfy old shoes that slip off
When we've wangled the laces undone
And best silky socks that we peel off his feet
And secrete in the sofa for fun.

Daddy is: mind-blowing After Shave Lotion
Soft sweaters and Classic FM.
And musical films with Sinatra, Gene Kelly,
Astaire: song and dance men like them.

Daddy is: yoghurt – we lick out the pot
Tongues in tandem we work stem to stern.
When we've polished it off Alice washes my face
Then I do it for her in return.

Daddy is: sitting by blazing log fires
Watching boxing or Match of the Day
With Alice and me curled up tight on his knee
At the end of a glorious day.

Mummy is…

by Alice

Mummy is: 'Don't' and 'How dare you' and 'No!'
When we're digging for gold in the grass.
And we mustn't eat primroses, pebbles or plant pots,
The postman or pieces of glass.

Mummy is: 'Hold it! Just look at those paws!
Well, you'd better not bring them inside.' –
Well, where can we put them? We can't take them off,
We don't come with a spare set supplied!

Mummy is: 'Don't wreck the sitting room sofa,
Don't scratch all the paint off the door.
Leave the carpet alone! Drop that plug! Mind the fire!
And don't bury those bones in the floor.'

BUT –

Mummy is: comfort and stroking of tummies
When tummies have gone on the blink.
And wonderful walks, introductions to rabbits
And keeping our coats in the pink.

Mummy is: teaching us reading and writing
And treats when we get it all right.
And choclatty bones and fantastical hugs
And 'God bless
and sweet dreams
and good night'.

Sofa

by Alice

Sarah's got a puppy
It's not a bit like us
No teeth, no tail and hardly any fur.
There's talk about 'The Baby'
Which I guess must be the breed
And we mustn't call it 'IT' 'cos it's a 'HER'.

They're going to call her SOFA
A funny sort of name
But Annie says my spelling's all at sea.
She says it's got a 'PHI'
Where I've put in an 'F'
A matter of opinion, you'll agree.

They brought her down to stay last week
And, dear me, what a noise!
She hasn't even got a proper bark.
She hollers when she's hungry
Which is several times a day
And screams instead of sleeping when it's dark.

Annie and I took turns on guard
Beside young Sofa's pram
From time to time I rocked it with my paw.
When Sarah picked me up to look
My eyes stood out on stalks
I'd never seen a dog like that before.

The poor wee thing was muffled up
Inside a big white shawl.
I don't think we had shawls when we were new.
I saw her little downy head
Her tiny, pink-tipped paws –
A pity that her eyelids don't unscrew.

It won't be long before she's grown
And then we'll have some fun.
We'll sneak her out the back to dodge the fuss.
We'll take her to the stable block
And roll her in the dirt
Then she can take the blame instead of us!

IT WON'T BE LONG BEFORE SHE'S GROWN
AND THEN WE'LL HAVE SOME FUN.

The Great Escape

by Annabel

After lunch on Bank Holiday Monday
We went for a wonderful walk.
If you skirt round the copse there are hundreds of rabbits
And dozens of pheasants to stalk.

There was Mummy and Sarah and Rosie –
The Labrador Sarah loves best –
Me and Alice, of course, we were both on the lead
So we set off ahead of the rest.

We had to keep waiting for Rosie
While everyone looked for her ball.
In the end it got lost in the hedge by the cornfield
And no-one could find it at all.

At last we arrived in the meadow
And after we'd squeezed through the stile
It was off with the leads and a race through the grass
To improve on our four-minute mile.

We always come back for a titbit
Whenever we're ordered to heel.
Mummy spreads out her arms and we sit at her feet,
Still as statues – that's part of the deal.

We chased through the fields in procession
And braked every time by the gate
Till we came to a place with a beautiful pool:
I tried hard to pull up, but too late!

The water came up to my collar
I felt a bit scared, to be frank.
Rosie shot past my head and went in with a splash
Striking out for the opposite bank.

Alice came to the edge for refreshment
The water was temptingly cool.
I suggested she went for a dip in the deep end
But Alice is nobody's fool.

I retreated when no-one was looking
And shook myself dry in the sun.
Then we gathered together and dashed up the field
Heading straight for the copse at a run.

It was there the calamity happened
By the stile where our leads are clipped on
A young rabbit rushed past saying, 'Follow me, girls!'
Without stopping to think, we were gone.

We chased him for miles through the woodland
To a glade where they chop up the logs
There were pheasants in pens looking after their young
And a sign which read PRIVATE – NO DOGS.

'What's it say?' enquired Alice, quite nervous.
'It's off limits to us,' I replied.
That young buck, who was probably laughing his head off
Had taken us both for a ride.

'Quick! The gamekeeper's coming,' gasped Alice,
'He'll shoot us for sure if we're found.'
She tore off through the trees without waiting for me
And I flattened myself to the ground.

The boots thudded nearer and nearer
I shut my eyes tightly and froze.
Then he passed and was gone and without hesitation
I set off to follow my nose.

The trail led me round through the cornfield
The scents were familiar here
But before I was back on the well-trodden path
Something horrid caught hold of my ear.

I was stuck in a thicket of brambles
Only minutes away from my tea.
I could hear Mummy's voice, very faint, in the distance,
I guessed she was searching for me.

Then out of the blue came that rabbit
He circled the bush once or twice.
'Want a pair of sharp teeth to release you, old sport?'
And he nibbled me free in a trice.

I flew down the track, then I found her
Mummy, trudging along quite alone
So I fell in behind as though nothing had happened
And trotted along on my own.

In two shakes of a lamb's tale she saw me.
It was clear that my wiles wouldn't work.
'You're a very bad girl and where's Alice?' she said
Then she snapped on my lead with a jerk.

We were making for home at the double
When a vision appeared from the West –
Alice – bowling along in an open-topped car –
Well! I'll leave her to tell you the rest.

The Great Escape
by Alice

I've plodded through Annabel's story
It's spot on as far as it goes
But things happened to me on Bank Holiday Monday
That not even Annabel knows.

As soon as the gamekeeper surfaced
I showed him a clean pair of heels
I knew Annie would hide and stay quiet as a mouse
But I can't face these dreadful ordeals.

I ran till I ran out of puffing
A terrible pain in my side.
I was all of a tremble and lonely and lost
So I sat in a cornfield and cried.

I didn't stay long in the doldrums
My spirits soon altered their tack
For a breeze brought a faint but familiar scent
And I set off to find my way back.

I circled the edge of the cornfield –
We never career through the crop –
But my progress was barred by a very large dog
Who stepped forward and forced me to stop.

'Let's mosey along,' he said slyly
I didn't much care for his tone
He was sniffing around in an impudent way
And I told him I travelled alone.

He wouldn't take 'No' for an answer
He came on exceedingly strong
So I said I was late for a previous engagement
And had to be getting along.

I squeezed through a hole in the hedgerow
Which left my pursuer outclassed
Then I tore round a field full of turnips and found
I was back by the stables at last.

I scratched at the door to the garden
It rattled but nobody came.
I was almost asleep when a car glided past
And I heard someone calling my name.

The driver peered down from his window
'Are you Alice?' I nodded my head.
'Well, my girl, I know someone who's looking for you,
You'd best hop in the motor,' he said.

I jumped on his lap in a jiffy –
I'm famously light on my feet –
As his wife and their children were squashed in the back
I took charge of the passenger seat.

The car was fantastic – a Citroen –
I wondered if Mummy would swap?!
I stood poised on the seat as we cruised up the lane
With my head through a hole in the top.

We rounded the corner and saw them,
Two figures approaching at speed.
It was Mummy, of course, with That Look on her face
And poor Annabel tight on the lead.

I leapt from the car in a frenzy –
I wasn't exactly well met.
I shall just draw a veil over what happened next
'Cos it's something I'd rather forget.

One-Upmanship

by Alice

Annabel's writing a sonnet –
Whatever a sonnet may be –
I think it's a bit of a challenge
And she keeps it a secret from me.

I wish I was clever like Annie,
She always comes top in a test.
She's frightfully keen on the long words
But I think the short ones are best.

Still, Mummy has boosted my spirits.
She says I have something called 'flair',
It's anyone's guess where it comes from
But I'm certainly glad that it's there.

So may be I'll catch up with Annie,
'Cos 'Fame', as they say, 'is the spur.'
I'll fasten my nose to the grindstone
And dash off a sonnet like her.

My Sonnet
by Annabel

With apologies to William Shakespeare

When in disgrace for some imagined wrong
I beat it to my beanbag in a huff,
Hoping I won't be ostracized for long
Indignant at the undeserved rebuff;
Wishing myself more like to Abigail,
Famous like her, more elegant in style,
With graceful carriage, finely fronded tail
And skill for writing poetry by the mile.
Yet, when all hope of harmony is dead,
Alice, I see you race across the room
Light as a feather settling on my bed,
Licking my face to chase away the gloom
And though you misbehave from time to time
I'll always face the music for your crime.

My Sonnet
by Alice

With no apologies to anyone

Shall I compare you to a hard-boiled egg?
O Annabel, you win hands down, no sweat.
It makes no odds how prettily I beg
'Cos half an egg is all I ever get.
Sometimes it's soft and runny which I hate,
Speckled with bits of shell which make me cough.
Occasionally it's past its sell-by-date
And eggs, you know, can taste distinctly 'off'.
But you, my friend, will always be top dog,
Bright-eyed and bushy-tailed, well-bred and true;
Whereas, I fear, however hard I slog,
I'll never be a genius like you.
Dear Annie, though I tease and pull your leg,
I love you better than a hard-boiled egg.

Sun Dog
by Annabel

Oh how I love the summer, for a tan improves my looks
I'm happy in the garden all the day.
I stretch out on my sunbed with my pencils and my books
Composing rhymes to while the time away.

Poor Alice cannot stand the heat for Alice is a blonde
She lies there like a duchess in the shade.
With parasol and floppy hat, spectacularly donned,
She sips a glass of sparkling lemonade.

It must be hard for Alice with her flaxen skin and hair
Still, Alice is a beauty, don't forget.
And though I know some gentlemen prefer their females fair,
I'd rather be the thinking man's brunette!

Tailpiece

by Alice

Annie is not exactly right, I do enjoy the sun
Especially when it hides behind a tree.
I like it when it wakes me up and when the day is done
I only wish it wouldn't glare at ME!

The Question

by Annabel

In a box in Mummy's cupboard in the bedroom
Is something called an heirloom, I've been told.
It was handed down by Abigail for Alice and for me,
A collar made of pearls inlaid with gold.

Sometimes we creep upstairs when no-one's looking
And if the cupboard's open – that's our chance!
I stand guard while Alice tries it on then she keeps watch for me,
Our getaway is set up in advance.

When Alice dons the necklace she's a knockout,
She'd win a beauty contest without doubt.
She's as pretty as a picture when she whirls around the floor
No wonder fellows fight to take her out.

When it's my turn for the wearing of the collar
I pose before the mirror, filled with pride.
If I stay quite still and hold my breath, another face appears
And Abigail is sitting by my side.

It's a secret: I'm the only one to see her.
I don't tell Alice, I'm afraid she'd scoff.
But it's good to know that Abigail is never far away
I love those pearls and hate to take them off.

There's one problem which, so far, has been avoided
I think the answer lies between us girls.
If we're going to a party and we're putting on the dog
I'd like to know –
'WHO GETS TO WEAR THE PEARLS?!'

The Answer

by Alice

It's simple: if we synchronize our diaries,
I'm sure we'll work it out without a fight
And if Annie's off to meet a beau she's eager to impress
She's welcome to the collar for the night.

But if I should have a date with an admirer
Poor Annie mustn't bellyache and grouse.
She'll help me fix my make up, put the pearls around my neck
Then she can stay at home and mind the house!

The Hysterectomy Kids

by Alice

They took us off to see the vet
We quite enjoyed the ride
But then they left us with the nurse
And I broke down and cried.

She stuck a needle in our paws
And left us in a heap
But Annie's arm was round me
As I drifted off to sleep.

The operation's over now
They did it with a spade.
They've taken out the nurseries
Where the puppy dogs are made.

At tea time Mummy came for us
And drove us home to bed
Poor Annie's supper went untouched
So I obliged instead.

I know that Annie's rather sad
But puppies would not do.
We'd never fit on Daddy's knee
If we were more than two!

We had to keep the stitches in
For seven days or more.
Annabel's tummy didn't hurt
But mine was very sore.

I think the vet was really mean
To stitch me up so tight.
And just to even up the score
I pulled one out each night.

At last he's passed us both A1
As frisky as can be.
So things are back to normal now
For Annabel and me.

The Vicarage Dog

by Annabel

The Vicarage Dog is chestnut brown
We meet him on our walk
He strolls along with eyes cast down
And never stops to talk.

The Vicarage Dog is sleek and slim
With hordes of female fans
Alice has set her cap at him
I, too, have made my plans.

So far we've failed to clip his wings
I think we've missed the bus.
His mind is fixed on Vicarage Things
Too deep for dogs like us.

But when our book comes out one day
And sales begin to soar
The Vicarage Dog may glance our way
And raise his Vicarage Paw.

First Christmas

by Annabel

We were so looking forward to Christmas
They told us what fun it would be
With the turkey and sausages, pudding and pies
And the presents piled high round the tree.

We practised Away In A Manger
So Mummy would have a surprise.
I'm afraid Alice tends to sing slightly off key
But she's keen and she's loud and she tries.

We hung up our little red stockings
The ones that we wear when it snows.
Alice kept running over to peer up the chimney
And nearly set fire to her nose.

We promised to sleep really soundly
Though Alice kept one eye awake.
We had left Father Christmas a glass of malt whiskey
Some nuts and two slices of cake.

We woke with a start in the morning
The oven cut in with a blast
That poor turkey was in for a bit of a shock
But for us it was Christmas at last.

The light was still on in the hallway
We peered through the glass panelled door.
We could see that the whiskey had gone and guess what –
There were cake crumbs all over the floor.

We jumped up and down with excitement
Till Mummy appeared on the scene.
First we sang her our carol then raced through the hall
For we knew Father Christmas had been.

We each had a spanking new collar
A ball and a bone and some chews
Then we carried them back to our toy box and voted
That Christmas was really good news.

After church it was over to Daddy
Who made a delectable drink
Then he poured it with care into beautiful glasses –
Champagne laced with framboise, I think.

And this was to prove our undoing,
Champagne-coated fingers to lick.
My poor head started spinning around like a whirlpool
And Alice felt frightfully sick.

We flaked out at last on our beanbags
Forgetting how quickly time flies
For we slept through the turkey, the sausage and bacon
And snored through the pudding and pies.

Next Christmas we'll stay off the bubbly
And try to do everything right.
We shall watch by the stove when the turkey goes in
And we won't let it out of our sight.